Bangers and Mash
have eggs for tea.

Mash taps his egg
with a spoon.

2

Yum! Yum!
It is fun to eat.

Bangers taps his egg
with a spoon.

Oh! It is bad.
A bad egg!

5

An ant pops out of
the egg.

It runs on the table.

A lot of ants pop out.

8

They run on the table.

Bangers puts the ants
in a tin with a spoon.

10

He puts the tin
on Dad's chair.

The ants get out of
the tin.

In comes Dad.

He sits on his chair.

14

Oh! Dad gets up!

He has ants in his pants.